Number
Journey

A & C Black • London

Andrew Brodie: Number Journey for ages 6-7 © A&C Black Publishers Ltd 2008

Contents

Andrew Brodie: Number Journey for ages 6-7 © A&C Black Publishers Ltd 2008

Introduction

Number Journey has been specially written to help teachers ensure progression in the teaching of number by addressing two key areas: the involvement of parents and the use of day-to-day assessment to promote success.

For many parents, the current methods used for teaching mathematics can be something of a mystery. Parents recognise certain aspects from their own school days but are surprised by some of the other approaches that are now being used in schools. The clash between the methods with which the parents are familiar and the methods their children are using in school can lead to many frustrations at home. The Williams review of 'Mathematics Teaching in Early Years Settings and Primary Schools' emphasises the role that parents can play in helping their children to learn mathematics. This can be summarised in the following four statements:

- Parents should be at the centre of any plan to improve children's outcomes.

- The panel heard time and again from children that they would like their parents to be taught the methods they are learning in mathematics, which have changed considerably since their parents were at school.

- The panel believes that the lack of clarification and setting out of the methods of teaching is a missed opportunity for engaging parents and improving their children's attainment.

- There is an opportunity for schools to work together with parents to dispel myths about the mystery of mathematics and give both children and parents a good grounding and positive attitude to this subject.

Number Journey addresses all four statements by providing materials that schools can use to ensure parents are given the opportunity to take an active part in their children's mathematical education. Current methods are explained clearly and the explanations are accompanied by activities that can be used at home to provide positive support for work at school. The teachers' notes for each unit specify clear learning objectives and list both outcomes and success criteria to enable teachers to make reliable assessments of pupils' work. The worksheets themselves are used to determine whether pupils have met the success criteria.

Andrew Brodie: Number Journey for ages 6-7 © A&C Black Publishers Ltd 2008

How is the book organised?

The materials in this book are organised into 15 units all designed to address the teaching of number – an area of maths in which many parents feel least confident but where they can actually be most helpful. *The Framework for mathematics teaching* includes a very wide range of learning objectives for understanding number, using number facts and calculating. In this book we have focused on the objectives where parental involvement will be most effective.

Each unit features an introductory page for teachers (*Teacher's Notes*), a letter for parents (*Help at Home Sheet*) that can be photocopied and sent home and two pupil worksheets (*Worksheets 1 and 2*). The calculation methods demonstrated on all the sheets are based on those recommended by the National Strategy.

Teacher's notes

These notes specify the learning objectives, learning outcomes and success criteria for each unit as well as suggesting opportunities for using and applying the skill being practised. The questions listed under 'Success criteria' are intended as prompts on which to base ongoing pupil assessment.

Help at home sheet

This is a letter for parents explaining what is being taught and, where appropriate, it also shows worked examples for parents to follow. There are also some ideas for relevant activities that can be completed at home. Introducing maths into everyday situations can increase a child's confidence and they can end up tackling complex number operations without even realising they are 'doing maths'.

Worksheets 1 and 2

The two worksheets provide activities that can be used by pupils for learning, for practising and for assessment. Where possible the children are encouraged to participate in their own assessment, identifying what they can do. Once a sheet is completed, discuss it with the child and help them to think about their own learning process. Ask questions such as 'How did you get on? Did you like this work? Did you find any of it too challenging?' With the second worksheet, discuss with the child whether they feel able to tick the 'I can' boxes. Celebrate their successes and support them if they are not ready to tick the boxes yet, by explaining that they will have another chance to revisit the concept and get more practice until they feel more confident.

Andrew Brodie: Number Journey for ages 6-7 © A&C Black Publishers Ltd 2008

Estimating and counting

Teacher's notes

Building on previous learning
Before starting this unit check that the children can already:
- count reliably at least 20 objects, recognising that when rearranged the number of objects stays the same
- estimate a number of objects that can be checked by counting
- count on or back in ones, twos, fives and tens
- compare and order numbers, using the related vocabulary.

Learning objectives
- Count up to 100 objects by grouping them and counting in tens.
- Count up to 100 objects by grouping them and counting in fives.
- Count up to 100 objects by grouping them and counting in twos.
- Read and write two-digit numbers in figures and words.
- Estimate a number of objects; round two-digit numbers to the nearest 10.

Learning outcomes
The children will:
- be able to give sensible estimates for the number of objects presented to them or for the number of items shown in a picture.
- have effective strategies for counting by grouping.
- be able to write the numbers from 0 to 100 using correctly formed numerals.

Success criteria
Can the children...
  … estimate sensibly when you scatter in front of them the following numbers of counters, small bricks, beads, etc: 21, 36, 85?
  … count successfully, by grouping in twos or fives, the following numbers of objects or items in pictures: 28, 35, 75? (You could use worksheet 1 for this assessment.)
  … count successfully, by grouping in tens, the following numbers of objects or items in pictures: 60, 80? (You could use worksheet 2 for this assessment.)
  … write clearly the following numbers: 28, 35, 75?

Resources needed
- A variety of counters, bricks, beads, etc.

Opportunities for using and applying the skills
There are many occasions when counting can be used in everyday life:
- estimating then counting how many people are present today by grouping them on to mats in a PE lesson.
- estimating then counting the number of balls in a basket in the PE store
- estimating then counting the number of books on the bookshelf

5

Estimating and counting
Help at home sheet

Child's name: **Date:**

Dear Parents

At school we follow the National Curriculum and the Primary Framework for mathematics. One aspect of our work in mathematics is the learning of number skills and part of that is, of course, counting. We are keen to involve parents in their children's learning so you may like to help your child by using some of the ideas on this sheet.

National Curriculum

The Primary Framework for mathematics says that Year 1 pupils should:

- count up to 100 objects by grouping them and counting in tens, fives or twos;
- read and write two-digit and three-digit numbers in figures and words;
- estimate a number of objects; round two-digit numbers to the nearest 10.

You could...

… ask your child to estimate then count numbers of objects, such as:

How many books are on the shelf?

How many slabs are on the patio?

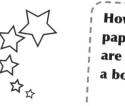

How many paper-clips are in a box?

How many chocolate buttons are in a packet?

Encourage your child to count the items in different ways. They could count them one at a time. They could count them in twos (and if there is one left at the end it gives you a chance to mention odd numbers). They could count them in groups of 5 or they could count them in groups of 10.

… ask your child to write the numbers clearly and correctly.

0   1   2   3   4   5   6   7   8   9

You may like to let us know how your child gets on with these activities – if so please return this sheet with any comments on the back.

Andrew Brodie: Number Journey for ages 6-7 © A&C Black Publishers Ltd 2008

Estimating and counting

Name: _____

Date: _____

On this page I will be estimating numbers of shapes.
On this page I will be counting in twos and I will be counting in fives.
On this page I will be writing numbers carefully.

How many triangles do you think there are? _____
Count them in twos by drawing rings around 2 at a time.

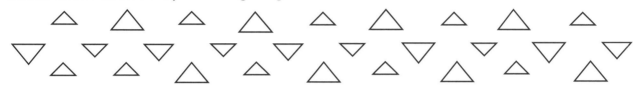

There are _____ triangles

How many squares do you think there are? _____
Count them in fives by drawing rings around 5 at a time.

There are _____ squares

How many circles do you think there are? _____
Count them in fives by drawing rings around 5 at a time.

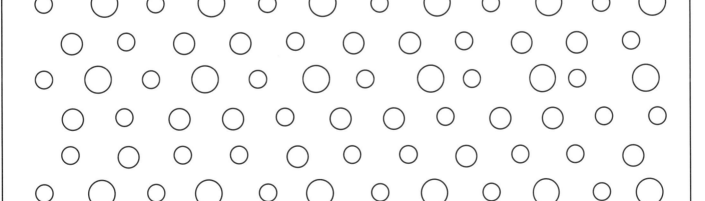

There are _____ circles

Andrew Brodie: Number Journey for ages 6-7 © A&C Black Publishers Ltd 2008

Estimating and counting

Name: _____

Date: _____

How many stars do you think there are? _____
Count them in tens by drawing rings around 10 at a time.

There are _____ stars

How many rectangles do you think there are? _____
Count them in tens by drawing rings around 10 at a time.

There are _____ rectangles

I can...   I can estimate sensibly. ☐

I can count carefully by grouping in twos. ☐

I can count carefully by grouping in fives. ☐

I can count carefully by grouping in tens. ☐

I can write numbers clearly. ☐

8

Rounding two-digit numbers to the nearest 10

Teacher's notes

Building on previous learning
Before starting this unit check that the children can already:
- read and write numerals from 0 to 20, then beyond; use knowledge of place value to position these numbers on a number track and number line
- compare and order numbers, using the related vocabulary

Learning objectives
- Read and write two-digit numbers in figures and words.
- Round two-digit numbers to the nearest 10.
- Order two-digit numbers and position them on a number line.

Learning outcomes
The children will be able to:
- read and write two-digit numbers in figures and words.
- position two-digit numbers on a number line.
- round two-digit numbers to the nearest 10.

Success criteria
Can the children...
… write these numbers in the correct order: 32 49 17 63 28 94 56 77?
… write these numbers in the correct place on the number line: 37 82 51 78 63 99?
… round each of the numbers 37 82 51 78 63 99 to the nearest 10?

Resources needed
- Number lines from 0 to 100, some with all numerals shown, others with just the multiples of 10 shown.

Opportunities for using and applying the skills
- Measuring with a metre stick that is marked in multiples of 10 centimetres.

Andrew Brodie: Number Journey for ages 6-7 © A&C Black Publishers Ltd 2008

Rounding two-digit numbers to the nearest 10

Help at home sheet

Child's name: Date:

Dear Parents

At school we follow the National Curriculum and the Primary Framework for mathematics. One aspect of our work in mathematics is the learning of number skills and part of that concerns rounding numbers to the nearest 10. To be able to do this the children need to understand the relationship between numbers as shown on a number line. We are keen to involve parents in their children's learning so you may like to help your child by using some of the ideas on this sheet.

National Curriculum

The Primary Framework for mathematics says that Year 2 pupils should:

- read and write two-digit and three-digit numbers in figures and words;
- round two-digit numbers to the nearest 10.

You could...

```
0   10   20   30   40   50   60   70   80   90   100   110
```

... use a number line like the one above. Write numbers such as 48, 23, 19, 84, 76, 62, 37, 59, 91 on small pieces of paper then ask your child to put them in the correct places on your number line. Your child could stick them in position with sticky tack. Talk about where the numbers are, which multiple of 10 is each number closest to? E.g. the number 59 is closest to 60. Encourage your child to say: "59 rounded to the nearest 10 is 60." Your child will make better progress with lots of practice and lots of praise.

... ask your child to write some numbers between 0 and 100, then to put them in the correct place on the number line and to say which multiple of 10 each number is closest to.

You may like to let us know how your child gets on with these activities – if so please return this sheet with any comments on the back.

Rounding two-digit numbers to the nearest 10

Name: _____

Date: _____

On this page I will be writing numbers in order.
On this page I will be writing numbers in the correct places on a number line.

Look at this set of numbers: 32   49   17   63   28   94   56   77

Write the numbers in the correct order:

Write the numbers in the correct places on the number line.

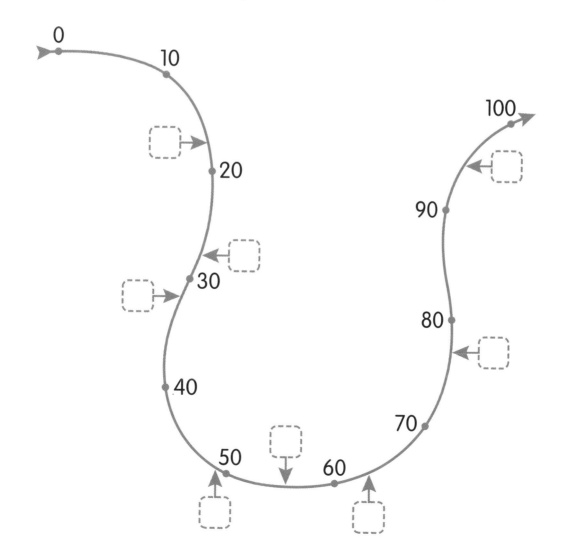

Andrew Brodie: Number Journey for ages 6-7 © A&C Black Publishers Ltd 2008

Rounding two-digit numbers to the nearest 10

Worksheet 2

Name: _____

Date: _____

Look at this set of numbers: 37   82   51   78   63   99

Write the numbers in the correct places on the number line.

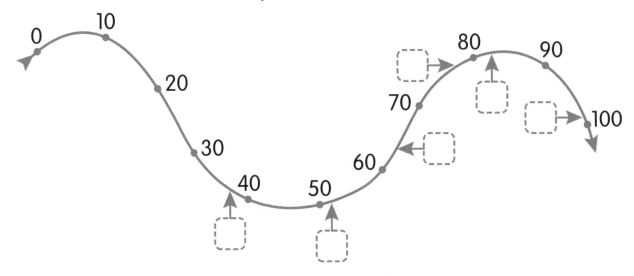

Round 37 to the nearest 10. ⟶

Round 82 to the nearest 10. ⟶

Round 51 to the nearest 10. ⟶

Round 78 to the nearest 10. ⟶

Round 63 to the nearest 10. ⟶

Round 99 to the nearest 10. ⟶

 I can...

I can write numbers in order. ☐

I can write numbers in the correct places on number lines. ☐

I can round numbers to the nearest 10. ☐

Andrew Brodie: Number Journey for ages 6-7 © A&C Black Publishers Ltd 2008

Recognising odd and even numbers

Teacher's notes

Building on previous learning
Before starting this unit check that the children can already:
- read and write numerals from 0 to 20, then beyond; use knowledge of place value to position these numbers on a number track and number line
- compare and order numbers, using the related vocabulary

Learning objectives
- Recognise odd and even numbers.
- Describe patterns and relationships involving numbers.

Learning outcomes
The children will be able to:
- identify whether a number is odd or even by looking at the 'ones' digit.
- use a hundred square to recognise the pattern made by even numbers and odd numbers.

Success criteria
Can the children identify...
... the following numbers as odd: 37 81 13 45?
... the following numbers as even: 58 96 60 72?
... all the even numbers between 25 and 31?
... all the odd numbers between 60 and 70?

Resources needed
- Hundred squares

Opportunities for using and applying the skills
- Looking at the numbers of houses in the street, observing that odd numbered houses are one side of the street and even number houses are the other side. Discuss why this might be so.
- Describing patterns and relationships – observing the pattern shown on the hundred square and realising that all the even numbers are multiples of 2.

Andrew Brodie: Number Journey for ages 6-7 © A&C Black Publishers Ltd 2008

Recognising odd and even numbers

Help at home sheet

Child's name: **Date:**

Dear Parents

At school we follow the National Curriculum and the Primary Framework for mathematics. One aspect of our work in mathematics is the learning of number skills and part of that concerns recognising odd numbers and even numbers. We are keen to involve parents in their children's learning so you may like to help your child by using some of the ideas on this sheet.

National Curriculum

The Primary Framework for mathematics says that Year 2 pupils should:

- recognise odd and even numbers.

You could...

... use this hundred square. Point to any number on the square and ask your child if it is odd or even. Remind your child that even numbers always have 0 or 2 or 4 or 6 or 8 as the 'ones' digit. All the other numbers are odd numbers. So 58 is an even number because it has 8 as the 'ones' digit. 69 is an odd number because it does not have 0 or 2 or 4 or 6 or 8 as the 'ones' digit.

1	2	3	4	5	6	7	8	9	10
11	12	13	14	15	16	17	18	19	20
21	22	23	24	25	26	27	28	29	30
31	32	33	34	35	36	37	38	39	40
41	42	43	44	45	46	47	48	49	50
51	52	53	54	55	56	57	58	59	60
61	62	63	64	65	66	67	68	69	70
71	72	73	74	75	76	77	78	79	80
81	82	83	84	85	86	87	88	89	90
91	92	93	94	95	96	97	98	99	100

... look at the numbers of the houses in your street with your child. Are the even numbers on one side and the odd numbers on the other side?

You may like to let us know how your child gets on with these activities – if so please return this sheet with any comments on the back.

Andrew Brodie: Number Journey for ages 6-7 © A&C Black Publishers Ltd 2008

Recognising odd and even numbers

Worksheet 1

Name: _____

Date: _____

On this page I will be colouring all the even numbers between 1 and 101.

On this page I will be finding all the odd numbers between 0 and 100.

Remember! Even numbers always have 0 or 2 or 4 or 6 or 8 as the 'ones' digit. All the other numbers are odd numbers.

42 is an even number because it has 2 as the 'ones' digit.

43 is an odd number because it does not have 0 or 2 or 4 or 6 or 8 as the 'ones' digit.

Colour all the even numbers on the hundred square.

1	2	3	4	5	6	7	8	9	10
11	12	13	14	15	16	17	18	19	20
21	22	23	24	25	26	27	28	29	30
31	32	33	34	35	36	37	38	39	40
41	42	43	44	45	46	47	48	49	50
51	52	53	54	55	56	57	58	59	60
61	62	63	64	65	66	67	68	69	70
71	72	73	74	75	76	77	78	79	80
81	82	83	84	85	86	87	88	89	90
91	92	93	94	95	96	97	98	99	100

For each of the numbers below, write odd or even.

37 _____   58 _____   81 _____   96 _____

13 _____   60 _____   72 _____   45 _____

Andrew Brodie: Number Journey for ages 6-7 © A&C Black Publishers Ltd 2008

Recognising odd and even numbers

Worksheet 2

Name: _____

Date: _____

1	2	3	4	5	6	7	8	9	10
11	12	13	14	15	16	17	18	19	20
21	22	23	24	25	26	27	28	29	30
31	32	33	34	35	36	37	38	39	40
41	42	43	44	45	46	47	48	49	50
51	52	53	54	55	56	57	58	59	60
61	62	63	64	65	66	67	68	69	70
71	72	73	74	75	76	77	78	79	80
81	82	83	84	85	86	87	88	89	90
91	92	93	94	95	96	97	98	99	100

Write all the even numbers between 25 and 31.

☐ ☐ ☐

Write all the odd numbers between 60 and 70.

☐ ☐ ☐ ☐ ☐

 I can recognise even numbers. ☐
I can recognise odd numbers. ☐

Andrew Brodie: Number Journey for ages 6-7 © A&C Black Publishers Ltd 2008

Finding one half, one quarter and three quarters of shapes

Teacher's notes

Building on previous learning

Before starting this unit check that the children can already:

- use the vocabulary of halves and quarters in context
- visualise and name common 2-D shapes
- identify shapes from pictures of them in different positions and orientations.

Learning objectives

- Find one half, one quarter and three quarters of shapes.
- Write $\frac{1}{2}$, $\frac{1}{4}$ and $\frac{3}{4}$ correctly.

Learning outcomes

The children will be able to:

- find one half of a circle, square or rectangle.
- find one quarter of a circle, square or rectangle.
- find three quarters of a circle, square or rectangle.
- write $\frac{1}{2}$, $\frac{1}{4}$ and $\frac{3}{4}$ correctly.

Success criteria

Can the children...

… identify one quarter of a circle?

… identify three quarters of a square?

… identify half a square, even where the square is cut into quarters and 2 of these are shaded?

… write $\frac{1}{2}$, $\frac{1}{4}$ and $\frac{3}{4}$ correctly?

Resources needed

- Circle, square and rectangle templates to draw round.

Opportunities for using and applying the skills

- Describing patterns and relationships – observing the pattern of shading of a shape that shows $\frac{1}{4}$, $\frac{2}{4}$, $\frac{3}{4}$ and noticing that $\frac{2}{4}$ is the same amount as $\frac{1}{2}$.
- Folding a piece of paper in half and using half of the paper for a drawing and half for writing.

Andrew Brodie: Number Journey for ages 6-7 © A&C Black Publishers Ltd 2008

Finding one half, one quarter and three quarters of shapes

Help at home sheet

Child's name: **Date:**

Dear Parents

At school we follow the National Curriculum and the Primary Framework for mathematics. One aspect of our work in mathematics is the learning of number skills, including learning to talk about halves and quarters in relation to real situations – this is ideal for home activities. We are keen to involve parents in their children's learning so you may like to help your child by using some of the ideas on this sheet.

National Curriculum

The Primary Framework for mathematics says that Year 2 pupils should:

• find one half, one quarter and three quarters of shapes.

You could...

… encourage your child to watch and take part in the cutting up of food such as apples, pizzas, pies, pieces of toast, etc, into halves and quarters. Discuss the mathematics with your child: "If I cut this cake in half there will be two equal pieces. Two halves make the whole cake. If I cut this pizza in quarters there will be four equal pieces. If you eat a quarter of the pizza there will be three quarters left." Again, lots of discussion will help, using appropriate words such as: part, equal parts, fraction, one whole pizza, one half, two halves, one quarter, two quarters, three quarters, four quarters.

… ask your child to draw a square on a piece of paper, then to colour in half the square.

… ask your child to draw round a plate to make a circle on a piece of paper, then to draw straight lines across the circle to divide it into four quarters and to colour three quarters.

You may like to let us know how your child gets on with these activities – if so please return this sheet with any comments on the back.

Finding one half, one quarter and three quarters of shapes

Worksheet 1

Name: _____

Date: _____

On this page I will be finding fractions of shapes.

Draw a line to match each fraction to the correct words.

$\dfrac{1}{4}$ one half

$\dfrac{1}{2}$ three quarters

$\dfrac{3}{4}$ one quarter

Write the correct fraction for each shape: $\dfrac{1}{4}$ or $\dfrac{1}{2}$ or $\dfrac{3}{4}$

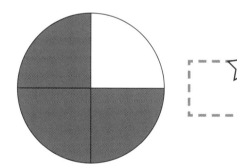   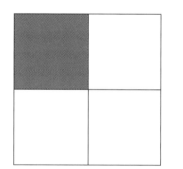 

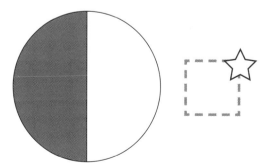   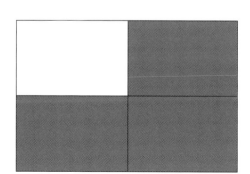

On the back of this sheet draw a square. Colour half your square and label it $\dfrac{1}{2}$.

Andrew Brodie: Number Journey for ages 6-7 © A&C Black Publishers Ltd 2008

Finding one half, one quarter and three quarters of shapes

Worksheet 2

Name: _____

Date: _____

Look at the shapes. How much of each shape is shaded?
Write the correct fraction for each one: $\frac{1}{4}$ or $\frac{1}{2}$ or $\frac{3}{4}$

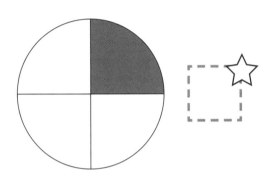

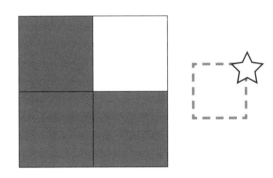

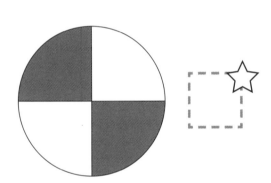

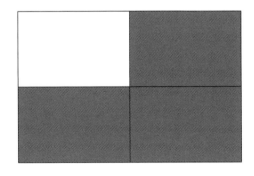 

I can...

I can recognise one half of a shape. ☐

I can recognise one quarter of a shape. ☐

I can recognise three quarters of a shape. ☐

I can write $\frac{1}{4}$, $\frac{1}{2}$ or $\frac{3}{4}$ ☐

Andrew Brodie: Number Journey for ages 6-7 © A&C Black Publishers Ltd 2008

Finding one half, one quarter and three quarters of sets of objects

Teacher's notes

Building on previous learning
Before starting this unit check that the children can already:
- use the vocabulary of halves and quarters in context
- read and write two-digit numbers in figures
- count reliably at least 20 objects, recognising that when rearranged the number of objects stays the same

Learning objectives
- Find one half, one quarter and three quarters of sets of objects.
- Write $\frac{1}{2}$, $\frac{1}{4}$ and $\frac{3}{4}$ correctly.

Learning outcomes
The children will be able to:
- find one half of a set of objects.
- find one quarter of a set of objects.
- find three quarters of a set of objects.
- write $\frac{1}{2}$, $\frac{1}{4}$ and $\frac{3}{4}$ correctly.

Success criteria
Can the children...

… find $\frac{1}{2}$ of 8?

… find $\frac{1}{4}$ of 16?

… find $\frac{3}{4}$ of 24?

… write $\frac{1}{2}$, $\frac{1}{4}$ and $\frac{3}{4}$ correctly?

Resources needed
- Counters, marbles, etc for counting and sharing into sets.

Opportunities for using and applying the skills
- Sharing equipment between 2 people or between 4 people, e.g.
"There are eight sheets of paper. Share the paper between the four people on your table so that you all have the same number of sheets. How many sheets of paper do you have each?"
"There are twenty counters. Share them equally with your partner. How many counters do you have each?"

Andrew Brodie: Number Journey for ages 6-7 © A&C Black Publishers Ltd 2008

Finding one half, one quarter and three quarters of sets of objects

Help at home sheet

Child's name: **Date:**

Dear Parents

At school we follow the National Curriculum and the Primary Framework for mathematics. One aspect of our work in mathematics is the learning of number skills, including learning to talk about halves and quarters in relation to real situations. We have already looked at cutting shapes or objects such as pizzas into halves or quarters and we are now looking at finding halves or quarters of sets of objects. We are keen to involve parents in their children's learning so you may like to help your child by using some of the ideas on this sheet.

National Curriculum

The Primary Framework for mathematics says that Year 2 pupils should:

• find one half, one quarter and three quarters of sets of objects.

You could...

… get a pile of 10 pennies and ask your child to share them with you and to say how many you each have. Use lots of discussion: "We've got ten pennies altogether. Let's share them between us – how many do we have each? We've got five each. Half of ten is five."

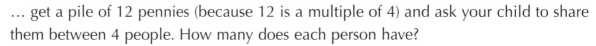

… get a pile of 12 pennies (because 12 is a multiple of 4) and ask your child to share them between 4 people. How many does each person have?

… count out 20 playing cards and ask your child to find:

half of 20   one quarter of 20   three quarters of 20

Again, discuss the mathematics. Can your child see that 3 quarters of 20 is 15 playing cards and that one quarter of 20 is the other 5 playing cards?

You may like to let us know how your child gets on with these activities – if so please return this sheet with any comments on the back.

Finding one half, one quarter and three quarters of sets of objects

Worksheet 1

Name: _____

Date: _____

On this page I will be finding fractions of sets of objects.

Draw a line to match each fraction to the correct words.

$\frac{3}{4}$ one half

$\frac{1}{4}$ three quarters

$\frac{1}{2}$ one quarter

Draw rings to make 2 equal sets of marbles.

There are 12 marbles altogether. $\frac{1}{2}$ of 12 = ☐

Draw rings to make 2 equal sets of pencils.

There are 14 pencils altogether. $\frac{1}{2}$ of 14 = ☐

Draw rings to make 4 equal sets of birds.

There are 20 birds aaltogether. $\frac{1}{4}$ of 20 = ☐

Finding one half, one quarter and three quarters of sets of objects

Worksheet 2

Name: _____

Date: _____

Draw rings to make 2 equal sets of cats.

There are 8 cats altogether. $\frac{1}{2}$ of 8 = ☐ ☆

Draw rings to make 4 equal sets of dogs.

There are 16 dogs altogether. $\frac{1}{4}$ of 16 = ☐ ☆

Draw rings to make 4 equal sets of rabbits.

There are 24 rabbits altogether. $\frac{1}{4}$ of 24 = ☐ ☆ $\frac{3}{4}$ of 24 = ☐ ☆

I can...

I can find one half of a set of objects. ☐
I can find one quarter of a set of objects. ☐
I can find three quarters of a set of objects. ☐
I can write $\frac{1}{4}$, $\frac{1}{2}$ or $\frac{3}{4}$ ☐

24

Addition facts for numbers to 10

Teacher's notes

Building on previous learning
Before starting this unit check that the children can already:
- read and write numerals from 0 to 20 and beyond
- count reliably at least 20 objects, recognising that when rearranged the number of objects stays the same
- relate addition to counting on
- recognise that addition can be done in any order
- use practical and informal written methods to support the addition of a one-digit number to a one-digit number

Learning objectives
- Derive and recall all addition facts for each number to at least 10.

Learning outcomes
The children will be able to:
- find all pairs of numbers that total 2, 3, 4, 5, 6, 7, 8, 9, 10.
- recall the pairs of numbers that total 2, 3, 4, 5, 6, 7, 8, 9, 10.

Success criteria
Can the children...
... find the addition facts for 8?
... find the addition facts for 9?
... find the addition facts for 10?
... recall the addition facts for numbers to 10? (Note that 'recall' does not necessarily mean to remember without thinking. The aim is for the child to have a strategy for retrieving the number facts quickly and efficiently.)

Resources needed

- Counters, marbles, etc for counting
- A class number line
- Individual number lines. (It's a good idea is to have a number line from 0 to 20 stuck to each child's table with sticky-backed plastic.)

Opportunities for using and applying the skills

- Presenting solutions to puzzles and problems in an organised way.
- Explaining decisions, methods and results in pictorial, spoken or written form, using mathematical language and number sentences.
- Describing patterns and relationships involving numbers.
- There are many every day occasions when adding can be used in context e.g. "How many pencils are on that group's table? Put three more on. How many are there now?"

Andrew Brodie: Number Journey for ages 6-7 © A&C Black Publishers Ltd 2008

Addition facts for numbers to 10

Help at home sheet

Child's name: **Date:**

Dear Parents

At school we follow the National Curriculum and the Primary Framework for mathematics. One aspect of our work in mathematics is the learning of number skills, including practising addition facts. The children will be able to make better progress in their maths if they are able to work out and then remember the additions of pairs of numbers that make the numbers up to 10 e.g. we encourage the children to learn all the addition facts for the number 8: 0 + 8, 1 + 7, 2 + 6, 3 + 5, 4 + 4, 5 + 3, 6 + 2, 7 + 1, 8 + 0. We are keen to involve parents in their children's learning so you may like to help your child by using some of the ideas on this sheet.

National Curriculum

The Primary Framework for mathematics says that Year 2 pupils should:

- derive and recall all addition facts for each number to at least 10.

You could...

… practise the following questions with your child. Allow your child to use his/her fingers if he/she wishes to. Ask you child to complete one column of questions then go through them together, giving tips on how to answer each one e.g. encourage him/her to start with the larger number and count on. Then do the next column of questions. Praise your child for any success. If you find that he/she is very confident, you could try timing. See how quickly he/she can complete one column of questions.

3 + 2 =	4 + 6 =	5 + 4 =	4 + 4 =
4 + 3 =	5 + 3 =	6 + 3 =	2 + 3 =
5 + 2 =	1 + 4 =	7 + 2 =	7 + 3 =
3 + 6 =	2 + 6 =	8 + 2 =	6 + 1 =
1 + 2 =	4 + 2 =	9 + 1 =	1 + 8 =
7 + 3 =	3 + 3 =	2 + 2 =	2 + 5 =
5 + 5 =	0 + 7 =	3 + 4 =	3 + 4 =
6 + 2 =	9 + 1 =	5 + 2 =	5 + 4 =

You may like to let us know how your child gets on with these activities – if so please return this sheet with any comments on the back.

Andrew Brodie: Number Journey for ages 6-7 © A&C Black Publishers Ltd 2008

Addition facts for numbers up to 10

Worksheet 1

Name: _____

Date: _____

On this page I will be finding addition facts for numbers.

These are the addition facts for 2.

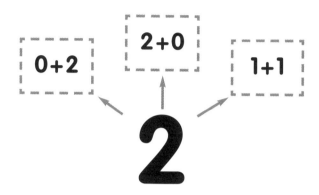

These are the addition facts for 3.

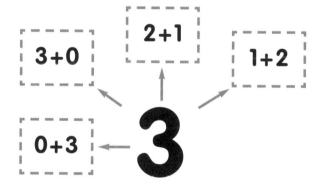

Find the missing addition facts for 4.

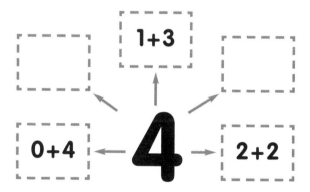

Find the addition facts for 5.

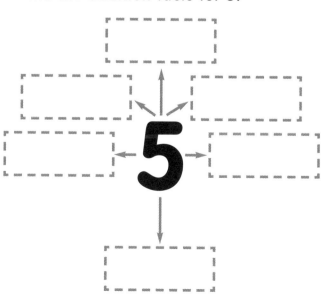

Find the addition facts for 6.

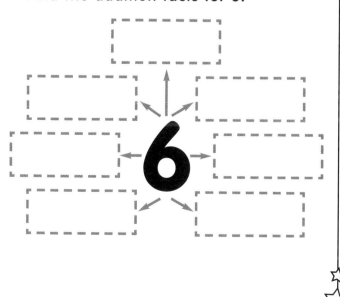

Andrew Brodie: Number Journey for ages 6-7 © A&C Black Publishers Ltd 2008

Addition facts for numbers up to 10

Name: _____

Date: _____

These are the addition facts for 7.

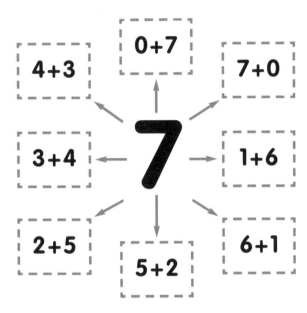

Find the addition facts for 8.

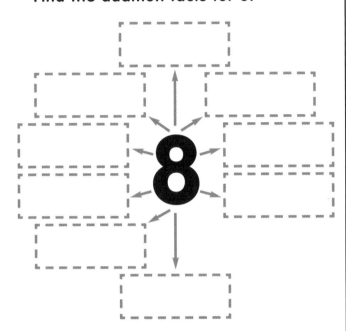

These are the addition facts for 9.

Find the addition facts for 10.

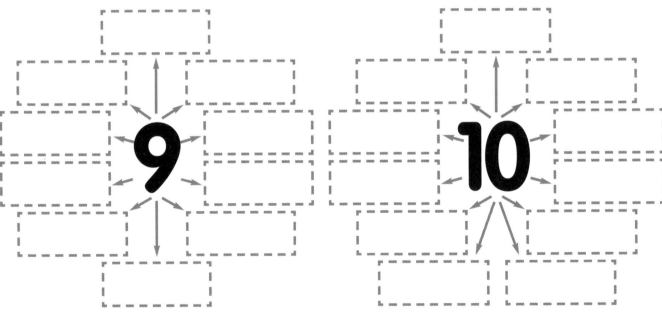

I can....
I can find the addition facts for 8. ☐
I can find the addition facts for 9. ☐
I can find the addition facts for 10. ☐

Andrew Brodie: Number Journey for ages 6-7 © A&C Black Publishers Ltd 2008

Subtraction facts for numbers to 10

Teacher's notes

Building on previous learning
Before starting this unit check that the children can already:
- read and write numerals from 0 to 20 and beyond
- count reliably at least 20 objects, recognising that when rearranged the number of objects stays the same
- understand subtraction as 'take away' and find a 'difference' by counting up
- use practical and informal written methods to support the subtraction of a one-digit number from a one-digit or two-digit number

Learning objectives
- Derive and recall all subtraction facts for each number to at least 10.

Learning outcomes
The children will be able to:
- find all subtractions from 1, 2, 3, 4, 5, 6, 7, 8, 9, 10.
- recall all subtractions from 1, 2, 3, 4, 5, 6, 7, 8, 9, 10.

Success criteria
Can the children...
… find the subtraction facts for 8?
… find the subtraction facts for 9?
… find the subtraction facts for 10?
… recall the subtraction facts for numbers to 10? (Note that 'recall' does not necessarily mean to remember without thinking. The aim is for the child to have a strategy for retrieving the number facts quickly and efficiently.)

Resources needed
- Counters, marbles, etc for counting
- A class number line
- Individual number lines. (It's a good idea is to have a number line from 0 to 20 stuck to each child's table with sticky-backed plastic.)

Opportunities for using and applying the skills
- Presenting solutions to puzzles and problems in an organised way.
- Explaining decisions, methods and results in pictorial, spoken or written form, using mathematical language and number sentences.
- Describing patterns and relationships involving numbers.
- Many every day occasions when subtracting can be usefully applied in context. In PE, for example, "How many people are sitting on that blue mat? If two people move to the red mat, how many people will be left on the blue mat?"

Andrew Brodie: Number Journey for ages 6-7 © A&C Black Publishers Ltd 2008

Subtraction facts for numbers to 10

Help at home sheet

Child's Name: **Date:**

Dear Parents

At school we follow the National Curriculum and the Primary Framework for mathematics. One aspect of our work in mathematics is the learning of number skills, including practising subtraction facts. The children will be able to make better progress in maths if they are able to work out and then remember the subtractions from all the numbers up to 10 e.g. we encourage the children to learn all the subtraction facts for the number 6: $6 - 6 = 0$, $6 - 5 = 1$, $6 - 4 = 2$, $6 - 3 = 3$, $6 - 2 = 4$, $6 - 1 = 5$, $6 - 0 = 6$. We are keen to involve parents in their children's learning so you may like to help your child by using some of the ideas on this sheet.

National Curriculum

The Primary Framework for mathematics says that Year 2 pupils should:

- derive and recall all subtraction facts for each number to at least 10.

You could...

… practise the following questions with your child. Allow your child to use his/her fingers if he/she wishes to. Ask you child to complete one column of questions then go through them together, giving tips on how to answer each question e.g. he/she could 'find the difference' by starting with the smaller number and counting on to the larger number. Then do the next column of questions. If you find that he/she is very confident, you could try timing. See how quickly he/she can complete one column of questions.

$6 - 4 =$	$10 - 9 =$	$6 - 4 =$	$5 - 2 =$
$9 - 5 =$	$8 - 7 =$	$9 - 3 =$	$8 - 1 =$
$10 - 6 =$	$1 - 1 =$	$10 - 7 =$	$9 - 7 =$
$8 - 5 =$	$5 - 3 =$	$8 - 2 =$	$10 - 8 =$
$5 - 1 =$	$7 - 2 =$	$6 - 3 =$	$3 - 3 =$
$3 - 2 =$	$9 - 4 =$	$5 - 5 =$	$5 - 4 =$
$6 - 5 =$	$4 - 2 =$	$7 - 1 =$	$7 - 3 =$
$7 - 4 =$	$2 - 1 =$	$4 - 3 =$	$6 - 5 =$

You may like to let us know how your child gets on with these activities – if so please return this sheet with any comments on the back.

Andrew Brodie: Number Journey for ages 6-7 © A&C Black Publishers Ltd 2008

Subtraction facts for numbers up to 10

Name: _____

Date: _____

On this page I will be finding subtraction facts for numbers.

These are the subtraction facts for 2.

2-1=1

2-2=0

2-0=2

2

These are the subtraction facts for 3.

3-1=2

3-2=1

3-0=3

3-3=0

3

Find the missing subtraction facts for 4.

4-2=

4-3=1

4-1=

4-4=

4-0=4

4

Find the missing subtraction facts for 5.

5-5=0

5

Find the subtraction facts for 6.

6

Andrew Brodie: Number Journey for ages 6-7 © A&C Black Publishers Ltd 2008

Subtraction facts for numbers up to 10

Worksheet 2

Name: _____

Date: _____

These are the subtraction facts for 7.

7-7=0

7-0=7

7-6=1

7-1=6

7

7-5=2

7-2=5

7-4=3

7-3=4

Find the subtraction facts for 8.

8

Find the subtraction facts for 9.

9

Find the subtraction facts for 10.

10

I can...

I can find the subtraction facts for 8. ☐

I can find the subtraction facts for 9. ☐

I can find the subtraction facts for 10. ☐

Andrew Brodie: Number Journey for ages 6-7 © A&C Black Publishers Ltd 2008

Addition facts to make totals up to 20

Teacher's notes

Building on previous learning
Before starting this unit check that the children can already:
- read and write numerals from 0 to 20 and beyond
- count reliably at least 20 objects, recognising that when rearranged the number of objects stays the same
- relate addition to counting on
- recognise that addition can be done in any order
- use practical and informal written methods to support the addition of a one-digit number to a one-digit or two-digit number

Learning objectives
- Derive and recall all pairs of numbers with a total of 20.
- Derive and recall all addition facts for each number to at least 10.
- Use the symbols + and = to record addition sentences.
- Calculate the value of an unknown in a number sentence.

Learning outcomes
The children will be able to:
- find all pairs of numbers that add together to make 20.
- find addition and subtraction facts for numbers beyond 10.

Success criteria
Can the children…
… find the addition pairs for 20?
… recall the addition pairs for 20? (Note that 'recall' does not necessarily mean to remember without thinking – The aim is for the child to have a strategy for retrieving the number facts quickly and efficiently.)
… find the addition pairs for 12?

Resources needed
- Counters, marbles, etc for counting
- A class number line
- Individual number lines. (It's a good idea is to have a number line from 0 to 20 stuck to each child's table with sticky-backed plastic.)

Opportunities for using and applying the skills
- Presenting solutions to puzzles and problems in an organised way.
- Explaining decisions, methods and results in pictorial, spoken or written form, using mathematical language and number sentences.
- Describing patterns and relationships involving numbers.

Andrew Brodie: Number Journey for ages 6-7 © A&C Black Publishers Ltd 2008

Addition facts to make totals up to 20

Help at home sheet

Child's name: **Date:**

Dear Parents

At school we follow the National Curriculum and the Primary Framework for mathematics. One aspect of our work in mathematics is the learning of number skills, including practising addition facts up to 20. We are keen to involve parents in their children's learning so you may like to help your child by using some of the ideas on this sheet.

National Curriculum

The Primary Framework for mathematics says that Year 2 pupils should:

- derive and recall all addition facts for each number to at least 10, all pairs with totals to 20;
- use the symbols + and = to record and interpret number sentences involving addition;
- calculate the value of an unknown in a number sentence.

You could...

… make a number line with your child showing all numbers from 0 to 20.

… practise the following questions with your child. Allow your child to use his/her fingers if he/she wishes to or to count on using the number line that you have made. Ask you child to complete one column of questions then go through them together, giving tips on how to answer each one e.g. where a number and then a box for an unknown number are provided, he/she should start at the number given then count on to twenty. Praise your child for any success before doing the next column of questions. If you find that he/she is very confident, you could try timing and see how quickly he/she can complete one column of questions. Most questions are repeated and this helps to establish them in a child's memory.

$15 + 5 = \square$	$15 + \square = 20$	$11 + \square = 20$	$\square + 4 = 20$
$16 + \square = 20$	$8 + 12 = \square$	$19 + \square = 20$	$18 + \square = 20$
$17 + 3 = \square$	$16 + \square = 20$	$17 + 3 = \square$	$15 + \square = 20$
$14 + \square = 20$	$12 + \square = 20$	$13 + \square = 20$	$13 + \square = 20$
$9 + \square = 20$	$10 + \square = 20$	$19 + 1 = \square$	$\square + 5 = 20$
$13 + 7 = \square$	$17 + 3 = \square$	$\square + 2 = 20$	$18 + 2 = \square$
$18 + \square = 20$	$19 + \square = 20$	$18 + \square = 20$	$14 + \square = 20$
$19 + \square = 20$	$18 + \square = 20$	$\square + 6 = 20$	$16 + 4 = \square$

You may like to let us know how your child gets on with these activities – if so please return this sheet with any comments on the back.

Andrew Brodie: Number Journey for ages 6-7 © A&C Black Publishers Ltd 2008

Addition facts to make totals up to 20

Name: _____

Date: _____

On this page I will be finding pairs of numbers that make 20.

Write all the addition facts that use pairs of numbers to make 20.
Two facts have been written for you.

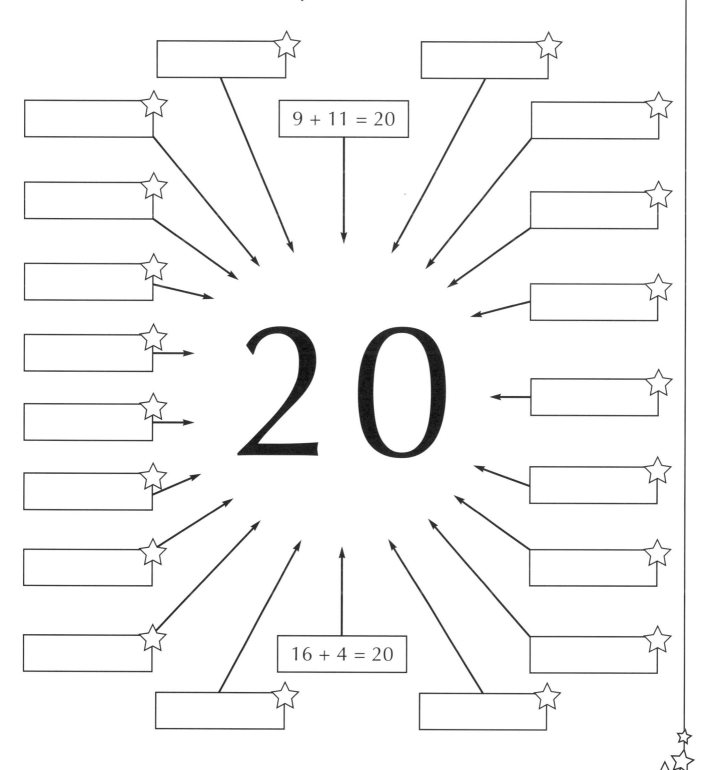

9 + 11 = 20

20

16 + 4 = 20

Andrew Brodie: Number Journey for ages 6-7 © A&C Black Publishers Ltd 2008

Addition facts to make totals up to 20

Name: _____

Date: _____

Find the addition pairs for number 12. Two facts have been written for you.

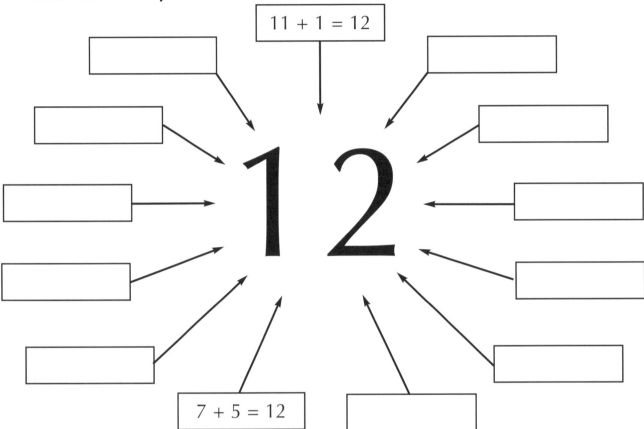

$11 + 1 = 12$

$7 + 5 = 12$

Answer these questions by writing the correct numbers in the boxes.

$14 + \boxed{} = 20$ $7 + \boxed{} = 20$ $5 + \boxed{} = 20$

$17 + \boxed{} = 20$ $6 + \boxed{} = 20$ $12 + \boxed{} = 20$

$15 + \boxed{} = 20$ $8 + \boxed{} = 20$ $9 + \boxed{} = 20$

I can...

I can find addition pairs for 12.   ☐

I can find addition pairs for 20.   ☐

I can recall addition pairs for 20.   ☐

Andrew Brodie: Number Journey for ages 6-7 © A&C Black Publishers Ltd 2008

Subtraction facts for 20

Teacher's notes

Building on previous learning

Before starting this unit check that the children can already:
- read and write numerals from 0 to 20 and beyond
- count reliably at least 20 objects, recognising that when rearranged the number of objects stays the same
- understand subtraction as 'take away' and find a 'difference' by counting up
- use practical and informal written methods to support the subtraction of a one-digit number from a one-digit or two-digit number.

Learning objectives

- Derive and recall all subtraction facts for 20.
- Derive and recall all subtraction facts for each number to at least 10.
- Use the symbols – and = to record subtraction sentences.
- Calculate the value of an unknown in a number sentence.

Learning outcomes

The children will be able to:
- find all subtraction facts from 20.
- find addition and subtraction facts for numbers beyond 10.

Success criteria

Can the children…
… find the subtractions from 20?
… find the subtractions from 12?
… recall the subtractions from 20? (Note that 'recall' does not necessarily mean to remember without thinking. The aim is for the child to have a strategy for retrieving the number facts quickly and efficiently.)

Resources needed

- Counters, marbles, etc for counting
- A class number line
- Individual number lines (It's a good idea to have a number line from 0 to 20 stuck to each child's table with sticky-backed plastic.)

Opportunities for using and applying the skills

- Presenting solutions to puzzles and problems in an organised way.
- Explaining decisions, methods and results in pictorial, spoken or written form, using mathematical language and number sentences.
- Describing patterns and relationships involving numbers.
- Solving problems involving subtraction in the context of money e.g. finding change from 20p.

Andrew Brodie: Number Journey for ages 6-7 © A&C Black Publishers Ltd 2008

Subtraction facts for numbers up to 20

Help at home sheet

Child's name: **Date:**

Dear Parents

At school we follow the National Curriculum and the Primary Framework for Mathematics. One aspect of our work in mathematics is the learning of number skills, including practising subtraction facts up to 20. We are keen to involve parents in their children's learning so you may like to help your child by using some of the ideas on this sheet.

National Curriculum

The Primary Framework for mathematics says that Year 2 pupils should:

- derive and recall all subtraction facts for each number to at least 10, all pairs with totals to 20.

You could...

… give your child some practice in finding change from 20p.

… make a number line with your child showing all numbers from 0 to 20.

… practise the following questions with your child. The questions involve subtracting from 20 or 12. Allow your child to use his/her fingers if he/she wishes to or to count on or back using the number line that you have made. Ask your child to complete one column of questions then go through them together, giving tips on how to answer each question e.g. he/she should start with the lower of the 2 numbers then count on to the bigger number or start with the bigger number and count back to the smaller number. Praise your child for any success before doing the next column of questions. If you find that he/she is very confident, you could try timing and see how quickly he/she can complete one column of questions.

$20 - 7 =$ ☐	$12 - 9 =$ ☐	$20 - 9 =$ ☐	$12 - 3 =$ ☐
$20 - 5 =$ ☐	$20 - 4 =$ ☐	$12 - 8 =$ ☐	$20 - 8 =$ ☐
$12 - 7 =$ ☐	$20 - 7 =$ ☐	$12 - 6 =$ ☐	$20 - 9 =$ ☐
$20 - 8 =$ ☐	$20 - 9 =$ ☐	$20 - 5 =$ ☐	$12 - 8 =$ ☐
$12 - 9 =$ ☐	$12 - 5 =$ ☐	$20 - 8 =$ ☐	$20 - 2 =$ ☐
$12 - 8 =$ ☐	$12 - 8 =$ ☐	$12 - 9 =$ ☐	$12 - 5 =$ ☐
$20 - 9 =$ ☐	$20 - 6 =$ ☐	$20 - 4 =$ ☐	$20 - 10 =$ ☐
$20 - 6 =$ ☐	$20 - 5 =$ ☐	$20 - 7 =$ ☐	$12 - 9 =$ ☐

You may like to let us know how your child gets on with these activities – if so please return this sheet with any comments on the back.

Andrew Brodie: Number Journey for ages 6-7 © A&C Black Publishers Ltd 2008

Subtraction facts for numbers up to 20

Worksheet 1

Name: _____

Date: _____

On this page I will be finding subtractions from 20.

Write all the subtraction from 20 facts. Two facts have been written for you.

$20 - 5 = 15$

$20 - 13 = 7$

Andrew Brodie: Number Journey for ages 6-7 © A&C Black Publishers Ltd 2008

Subtraction facts for numbers up to 20

Name: _____

Date: _____

Find the subtraction from 12 facts. Two facts have been written for you.

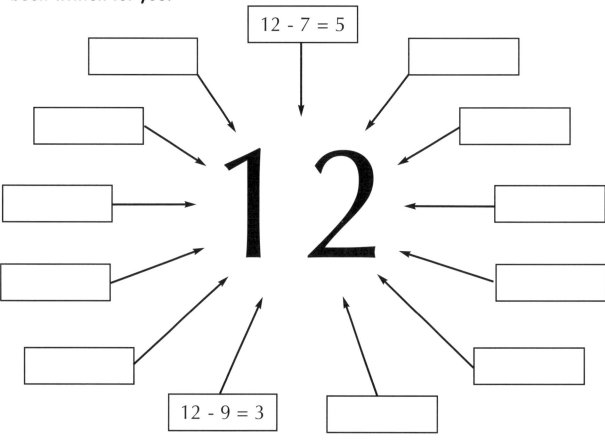

12 - 7 = 5

12 - 9 = 3

Answer these subtractions by writing the correct numbers in the boxes.

20 - 10 =

12 - 6 =

20 - 8 =

20 - 6 =

12 - 9 =

20 - 4 =

12 - 8 =

20 - 11 =

20 - 14 =

I can...

I can find subtractions from 12. ☐

I can find subtractions from 20. ☐

I can recall subtractions from 20. ☐

Andrew Brodie: Number Journey for ages 6-7 © A&C Black Publishers Ltd 2008

Addition and subtraction facts for pairs of multiples of 10

Teacher's notes

Building on previous learning
Before starting this unit check that the children can already:
- read and write numerals from 0 to 100
- count up to 100 objects by grouping them and counting in tens
- recognise multiples of 10
- order two-digit numbers and position them on a number line
- use practical and informal written methods to support the addition of a multiple of 10 to a one-digit or two-digit number

Learning objectives
- Derive and recall all addition and subtraction facts for all pairs of multiples of 10 with totals up to 100.
- Use the symbols + and = to record addition sentences.
- Use the symbols – and = to record subtraction sentences.
- Calculate the value of an unknown in a number sentence.

Learning outcomes
The children will be able to:
- find all pairs of multiples of 10 that add together to make 10, 20, 30, 40, 50, 60, 70, 80, 90.
- subtract multiples of 10 from larger multiples of 10.

Success criteria
Can the children…
… add multiples of 10 such as 60 + 40, 30 + 20, 40 + 50.
… subtract multiples of 10 from larger multiples of 10, such as 70 – 40, 100 – 50, 60 – 50.

Resources needed
- Counters, marbles, etc for counting
- A class number line from 0 to at least 100
- A hundred square. Encourage the pupils to notice that the answers to the questions above, all appear in the right-hand column of the square. This will give them clues to solving questions involving adding multiples of 10 to any number. (Worksheet 1 also provides ideas for using the hundred square.)

Opportunities for using and applying the skills
- Presenting solutions to puzzles and problems in an organised way.
- Explaining decisions, methods and results in pictorial, spoken or written form, using mathematical language and number sentences.
- Describing patterns and relationships involving numbers.
- Solving problems involving addition or subtraction in the context of money e.g. "How much is 20p add 40p?" "If I have 90p and I spend 60p, how much have I got left?"

Andrew Brodie: Number Journey for ages 6-7 © A&C Black Publishers Ltd 2008

Addition and subtraction facts for pairs of multiples of 10

Help at home sheet

Child's name: **Date:**

Dear Parents

At school we follow the National Curriculum and the Primary Framework for Mathematics. One aspect of our work in mathematics is the learning of number skills, including practising addition facts for multiples of 10 e.g. 50 add 40. We are keen to involve parents in their children's learning so you may like to help your child by using some of the ideas on this sheet.

National Curriculum

The Primary Framework for Mathematics says that Year 2 pupils should:

- derive and recall all addition and subtraction facts for all pairs of multiples of 10 with totals up to 100.

You could...

… make a number line with your child showing all multiples of 10 from 0 to 100. Ideally all the other numbers should be marked on as well so you will need a large piece of paper to make a curved number line or use several strips of paper joined together to make a long number line. You could display the number line on your child's bedroom wall so that he/she can refer to it at any time.

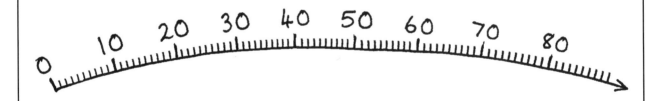

Once the number line is ready, ask your child questions such as:

"If I start at 20 and count on 30 what number do I get to?"

"If I start at 70 and count back 40 what number do I get to?"

When your child is confident, move on to questions such as '40 add 20', '80 subtract 60', etc.

You may like to let us know how your child gets on with these activities – if so please return this sheet with any comments on the back.

Andrew Brodie: Number Journey for ages 6-7 © A&C Black Publishers Ltd 2008

Addition and subtraction facts for pairs of multiples of 10

Worksheet 1

Name: _____

Date: _____

On this page I will be finding addition and subtraction facts for multiples of 10.
Look at the hundred square.

1	2	3	4	5	6	7	8	9	10
11	12	13	14	15	16	17	18	19	20
21	22	23	24	25	26	27	28	29	30
31	32	33	34	35	36	37	38	39	40
41	42	43	44	45	46	47	48	49	50
51	52	53	54	55	56	57	58	59	60
61	62	63	64	65	66	67	68	69	70
71	72	73	74	75	76	77	78	79	80
81	82	83	84	85	86	87	88	89	90
91	92	93	94	95	96	97	98	99	100

Colour the 10 red. Add 20.
Colour the number you find, red.

$10 + 20 =$

Colour the 20 blue. Add 40.
Colour the number you find, blue.

$20 + 40 =$

Colour the 70 green. Subtract 30.
Colour the number you find, green.

$70 - 30 =$

Colour the 90 yellow. Subtract 40.
Colour the number you find, yellow.

$90 - 40 =$

Can you make up your own question about multiples of 10?

Addition and subtraction facts for pairs of multiples of 10

Worksheet 2

Name: _____

Date: _____

1	2	3	4	5	6	7	8	9	10
11	12	13	14	15	16	17	18	19	20
21	22	23	24	25	26	27	28	29	30
31	32	33	34	35	36	37	38	39	40
41	42	43	44	45	46	47	48	49	50
51	52	53	54	55	56	57	58	59	60
61	62	63	64	65	66	67	68	69	70
71	72	73	74	75	76	77	78	79	80
81	82	83	84	85	86	87	88	89	90
91	92	93	94	95	96	97	98	99	100

Answer these questions.

60 + 40 = ☐   30 + 20 = ☐   40 + 50 = ☐

30 + ☐ = 70   ☐ + 80 = 90   20 + ☐ = 80

70 - 40 = ☐   100 - 50 = ☐   60 - 50 = ☐

100 - ☐ = 70   80 - ☐ = 10   90 - ☐ = 30

I can...

I can add multiples of 10 together. ☐

I can subtract a multiple of 10 from a larger multiple of 10. ☐

Andrew Brodie: Number Journey for ages 6-7 © A&C Black Publishers Ltd 2008

Doubles of all numbers to 20

Teacher's notes

Building on previous learning
Before starting this unit check that the children can already:
- derive the doubles of all numbers to at least 10
- recall the doubles of all numbers to at least 10

Learning objectives
- Derive the doubles of all numbers to 20.
- Recall the doubles of all numbers to 20.
- Understand that halving is the inverse of doubling.

Learning outcomes
The children will be able to:
- find doubles of all numbers from 1 to 20.
- recall doubles of all numbers from 1 to 20.
- find halves of even numbers from 2 to 40.

Success criteria
Can the children…
… derive the doubles of 12, 15, 17, 13, 18, 20?
… recall the doubles of 11, 12, 13, 14, 15, 16, 17, 18, 19, 20?
… derive the halves of 20, 32, 34, 40, 36, 26?
… recall the halves of 2, 4, 6, 8, 10, 12, 14, 16, 18, 20, 22, 24, 26, 28, 30, 32, 34, 36, 38, 40?

Resources needed
- A number line from 0 to 40
- A variety of objects for counting
- Counters

Opportunities for using and applying the skills
- Solving problems involving addition and multiplication in the context of numbers or money.
- Identifying and recording the information and calculation needed to solve a problem; carrying out the calculations and checking the solutions.

Doubles of all numbers to 20

Help at home sheet

Child's name: **Date:**

Dear Parents

At school we follow the National Curriculum and the Primary Framework for mathematics. One aspect of our work in mathematics is the learning of number skills, including learning the doubles of all numbers from 1 to 20. We are keen to involve parents in their children's learning so you may like to help your child by using some of the ideas on this sheet.

National Curriculum

The Primary Framework for mathematics says that Year 2 pupils should:

- understand that halving is the inverse of doubling and derive and recall doubles of all numbers to 20 and the corresponding halves.

You could...

… pick up a random number of paper-clips, e.g. 12. Ask your child to count them and then to find a matching number of paper-clips. Discuss the maths with your child, using appropriate vocabulary: "I've got 12 paper-clips. You've got 12 paper-clips. We've got 24 paper-clips altogether so double 12 is 24 and half of 24 is 12."

…keep practising and praising. Encourage your child to talk mathematically, using words such as 'double', 'half', 'equals' and 'altogether'.

…use a variety of items and practise with different numbers.

You may like to let us know how your child gets on with these activities – if so please return this sheet with any comments on the back.

Doubles of all numbers to 20

Worksheet 1

Name: _____

Date: _____

On this page I am going to find doubles of numbers.

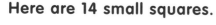

Here are 14 small squares.

Draw 14 more squares in this space.

There are [ ] squares altogether.   Double 14 = [ ]   Half of [ ] = 14

Use counters to help you to answer these questions.

Double 7 = [ ]   **Double 12 =** [ ]   **Double 13 =** [ ]

Double 10 = [ ]   **Double 15 =** [ ]   **Double 11 =** [ ]

Andrew Brodie: Number Journey for ages 6-7 © A&C Black Publishers Ltd 2008

Doubles of all numbers to 20

Worksheet 2

Name: _____

Date: _____

If you need to you can use counters to help
you with these questions.

Double 16 = [☆]   Half of [☆] = 16

Double 12 = [☆]   Double 15 = [☆]   Double 17 = [☆]

Double 13 = [☆]   Double 18 = [☆]   Double 20 = [☆]

Half of 20 = [☆]   Half of 32 = [☆]   Half of 34 = [☆]

Half of 40 = [☆]   Half of 36 = [☆]   Half of 26 = [☆]

I can...

I can find doubles of numbers up to 20. ☐

I can remember doubles of numbers up to 20. ☐

I can find halves of even numbers from 2 to 40. ☐

I can remember halves of even numbers from 2 to 40. ☐

Andrew Brodie: Number Journey for ages 6-7 © A&C Black Publishers Ltd 2008

Addition and subtraction of a one-digit number to or from any two-digit number

Teacher's notes

Building on previous learning
Before starting this unit check that the children can already:
- read and write numerals from 0 to 100
- count up to 100 objects by grouping them and counting in tens
- order two-digit numbers and position them on a number line
- use practical and informal written methods to support the addition or subtraction of a one-digit number to or from a one-digit or two-digit number
- derive and recall all addition and subtraction facts for each number to at least 10, all pairs with totals to 20 and all pairs of multiples of 10 with totals up to 100

Learning objectives
- Add or subtract mentally a one-digit number to or from any two-digit number.
- Use the symbols + and = to record and interpret addition sentences.
- Use the symbols – and = to record and interpret subtraction sentences.
- Solve problems involving addition or subtraction in the context of money.

Learning outcomes
The children will be able to:
- add mentally a one-digit number to any two-digit number.
- subtract mentally a one-digit number from any two-digit number.
- decide whether to add or subtract when solving problems involving money.

Success criteria
Can the children…
 … add one-digit numbers to two-digit numbers: 52 + 6, 68 + 8, 49 + 3, 17 + 5?
 … subtract one-digit numbers from two-digit numbers: 47 – 3, 72 – 8, 93 – 5, 33 – 6?
 … choose whether to add or subtract with worded problems such as those on worksheet 2?

Resources needed
- Counters, marbles, etc for counting
- A class number line from 0 to at least 100
- A hundred square. Make sure that the children know how to use the hundred square confidently. Are they aware that once they reach a multiple of 10 they have to 'jump' to the start of the next row rather than following the numbers around each 'corner' as they would on a Snakes and Ladders board?

Opportunities for using and applying the skills
- Presenting solutions to puzzles and problems in an organised way.
- Explaining decisions, methods and results in pictorial, spoken or written form, using mathematical language and number sentences.
- Describing patterns and relationships involving numbers.
- Solving problems involving addition or subtraction in the context of money.

49

Addition and subtraction of a one-digit number to or from any two-digit number

Help at home sheet

Child's name: **Date:**

Dear Parents

At school we follow the National Curriculum and the Primary Framework for mathematics. One aspect of our work in mathematics is the learning of number skills, including practising adding a one-digit number to any two-digit number, e.g. 36 + 7, and practising subtracting a one-digit number from any two-digit number, e.g. 61 – 9. We are keen to involve parents in their children's learning so you may like to help your child by using some of the ideas on this sheet.

National Curriculum

The Primary Framework for mathematics says that Year 2 pupils should:

- add or subtract mentally a one-digit number or a multiple of 10 to or from any two-digit number.

You could...

… use this hundred square. Notice that 1 to 10 are on the first line but then to get to 11 your child will have to 'jump' to the first number on the next line, etc.

1	2	3	4	5	6	7	8	9	10
11	12	13	14	15	16	17	18	19	20
21	22	23	24	25	26	27	28	29	30
31	32	33	34	35	36	37	38	39	40
41	42	43	44	45	46	47	48	49	50
51	52	53	54	55	56	57	58	59	60
61	62	63	64	65	66	67	68	69	70
71	72	73	74	75	76	77	78	79	80
81	82	83	84	85	86	87	88	89	90
91	92	93	94	95	96	97	98	99	100

… point to a random two-digit number, then ask your child to add a one-digit number to it e.g. you could point to 42 and ask your child to add 7. When you start practising together your child may choose to use his/her fingers or to count on using the hundred square. These are good strategies but with further practice your child will begin to gain confidence and will rely on them less and less.

You may like to let us know how your child gets on with these activities – if so please return this sheet with any comments on the back.

Andrew Brodie: Number Journey for ages 6-7 © A&C Black Publishers Ltd 2008

Addition and subtraction of a one-digit number to or from any two-digit number

Worksheet 1

Name: _____

Date: _____

On this page I will be adding one-digit numbers to two-digit numbers.

On this page I will be subtracting one-digit numbers from two-digit numbers.

The hundred square may help.

1	2	3	4	5	6	7	8	9	10
11	12	13	14	15	16	17	18	19	20
21	22	23	24	25	26	27	28	29	30
31	32	33	34	35	36	37	38	39	40
41	42	43	44	45	46	47	48	49	50
51	52	53	54	55	56	57	58	59	60
61	62	63	64	65	66	67	68	69	70
71	72	73	74	75	76	77	78	79	80
81	82	83	84	85	86	87	88	89	90
91	92	93	94	95	96	97	98	99	100

Answer these addition questions.

$32 + 6 =$ $41 + 7 =$ $93 + 4 =$ $52 + 6 =$

$68 + 8 =$ $49 + 3 =$ $17 + 5 =$ $86 + 4 =$

Answer these subtraction questions.

$27 - 6 =$ $39 - 5 =$ $58 - 3 =$ $99 - 7 =$

$60 - 2 =$ $90 - 9 =$ $81 - 7 =$ $14 - 6 =$

51

Andrew Brodie: Number Journey for ages 6-7 © A&C Black Publishers Ltd 2008

Addition and subtraction of a one-digit number to or from any two-digit number

Worksheet 2

Name: _____

Date: _____

Answer these questions.

26p + 3p = [ ] p   39p + 8p = [ ] p   47p + 6p = [ ] p

59p + 8p = [ ] p   62p + 7p = [ ] p   84p + 5p = [ ] p

17p + 5p = [ ] p   71p + 9p = [ ] p   91p + 9p = [ ] p

30p - 6p = [ ] p   50p - 7p = [ ] p   80p - 9p = [ ] p

42p - 5p = [ ] p   69p - 8p = [ ] p   35p - 6p = [ ] p

I have 28p in my pocket. Sam gives me 6p more. How much have I got now? [ ] p

I have 37p. I buy a sweet for 5p. How much money have I got left? [ ] p

I have 20p. I spend 8p. How much change do I have? [ ] p

I have 67p then Mum gives me 6p. How much have I got now? [ ] p

 I can...

I can add a one-digit number to any two-digit number. ☐

I can subtract a one-digit number from any two-digit number. ☐

I can solve problems about money. ☐

Andrew Brodie: Number Journey for ages 6-7 © A&C Black Publishers Ltd 2008

The 2 times-table and related division facts

Teacher's notes

Building on previous learning
Before starting this unit check that the children can already:
- count on or back in twos and use this knowledge to derive the multiples of 2 to the tenth multiple

Learning objectives
- Derive multiplication facts for the 2 times-table.
- Recall multiplication facts for the 2 times-table.
- Derive the related division facts for the 2 times-table.
- Recall the related division facts for the 2 times-table.

Learning outcomes
- The children will be able to:
- find the multiplication facts for the 2 times-table.
- recall the multiplication facts for the 2 times-table.
- find the division facts for the 2 times-table.
- recall the division facts for the 2 times-table.

Success criteria
Can the children…

… recall multiplication facts for the two times-table:

6×2, 8×2, 2×2, 10×2, 3×2, 9×2, 1×2, 5×2?

… recall division facts for the two times-table:

$18 \div 2$, $12 \div 2$, $6 \div 2$, $14 \div 2$, $20 \div 2$, $16 \div 2$, $4 \div 2$, $10 \div 2$?

Resources needed
- A number line from 0 to 20
- A display of the two times-table. (Note that we are using the traditional layout of the two times-table, i.e. $3 \times 2 = 6$ to represent 'three twos are six'. Some schools may prefer to use 'three twos are six' written as $2 \times 3 = 6$).

Opportunities for using and applying the skills
- Solving problems involving addition, subtraction, multiplication and division in the context of numbers or money.
- Identifying and recording the information and calculation needed to solve a problem; carrying out the calculations and checking the solutions.
- Describing patterns and relationships involving numbers.
- Presenting information in lists, tables and simple diagrams.

Andrew Brodie: Number Journey for ages 6-7 © A&C Black Publishers Ltd 2008

The 2 times-table and related division facts

Help at home sheet

Child's name: **Date:**

Dear Parents

At school we follow the National Curriculum and the Primary Framework for mathematics. One aspect of our work in mathematics is the learning of number skills, including learning the two times multiplication table and the division facts that arise from it. We are keen to involve parents in their children's learning so you may like to help your child by using some of the ideas on this sheet.

National Curriculum

The Primary Framework for mathematics says that Year 2 pupils should:

- derive and recall multiplication facts for the 2 times-table and the related division facts.

You could...

… practise the 2 times-table every day for a week – in the car, when walking, last thing at night before bed-time, first thing in the morning. It's important on each occasion to keep the practice short, perhaps just one or two minutes. Show your child the table below – with practice he/she will need to look at it less.

1 x 2 = 2	one times two is two
2 x 2 = 4	two twos are four
3 x 2 = 6	three twos are six
4 x 2 = 8	four twos are eight
5 x 2 =10	five twos are ten
6 x 2 =12	six twos are twelve
7 x 2 =14	seven twos are fourteen
8 x 2 =16	eight twos are sixteen
9 x 2 =18	nine twos are eighteen
10 x 2 =20	ten twos are twenty

Once you feel that your child is confident with saying the table, ask random questions such as: "What's five times two?" "Six twos?" "Eight multiplied by two?"

If you feel that your child is able to answer the multiplication questions easily, try some division questions: "How many twos make ten?" "Divide eighteen by two."

You may like to let us know how your child gets on with these activities – if so please return this sheet with any comments on the back.

Andrew Brodie: Number Journey for ages 6-7 © A&C Black Publishers Ltd 2008

The 2 times-table and related division facts

Worksheet 1

Name: _____

Date: _____

On this page I am going to make the 2 times-table.

Draw rings around the birds to make groups of two.

Write the 2 times-table.

1 x 2 = ☆　　　one times two is _____

2 x 2 = ☆　　　two twos are _____

3 x 2 = ☆　　　three twos are _____

4 x 2 = ☆　　　four twos are _____

5 x 2 = ☆　　　five twos are _____

6 x 2 = ☆　　　six twos are _____

7 x 2 = ☆　　　seven twos are _____

8 x 2 = ☆　　　eight twos are _____

9 x 2 = ☆　　　nine twos are _____

10 x 2 = ☆　　　ten twos are _____

Look at this multiplication fact: $8 \times 2 = 16$

We can use this fact to find two division facts: $16 \div 2 = 8$ and $16 \div 8 = 2$

55

Andrew Brodie: Number Journey for ages 6-7 © A&C Black Publishers Ltd 2008

The 2 times-table and related division facts

Worksheet 2

Name: _____

Date: _____

Look at the 2 times-table. Write division facts
next to the multiplication facts. The first five have been done for you.

1 x 2 = 2	<u>2 ÷ 2 = 1</u>	<u>2 ÷ 1 = 2</u>
2 x 2 = 4	<u>4 ÷ 2 = 2</u>	There is only one division fact for this one.
3 x 2 = 6	<u>6 ÷ 3 = 2</u>	<u>6 ÷ 2 = 3</u>
4 x 2 = 8	_____	_____
5 x 2 = 10	_____	_____
6 x 2 = 12	_____	_____
7 x 2 = 14	_____	_____
8 x 2 = 16	_____	_____
9 x 2 = 18	_____	_____
10 x 2 = 20	_____	_____

Fold the paper so that you can't see the two times-table!

Can you answer these questions quickly without looking at the 2 times-table?

6 x 2 =	8 x 2 =	2 x 2 =	10 x 2 =
18 ÷ 8 =	12 ÷ 2 =	6 ÷ 2 =	14 ÷ 2 =
3 x 2 =	9 x 2 =	1 x 2 =	5 x 2 =
20 ÷ 2 =	16 ÷ 2 =	4 ÷ 2 =	10 ÷ 2 =

I can remember the multiplication facts for the two times-table. ☐

I can remember the division facts for the two times-table. ☐

56

Andrew Brodie: Number Journey for ages 6-7 © A&C Black Publishers Ltd 2008

The 5 times-table and related division facts

Teacher's notes

Building on previous learning
Before starting this unit check that the children can already:
- count on or back in fives and use this knowledge to derive the multiples of 5 to the 10th multiple

Learning objectives
- Derive multiplication facts for the 5 times-table.
- Recall multiplication facts for the 5 times-table.
- Derive the related division facts for the 5 times-table.
- Recall the related division facts for the 5 times-table.

Learning outcomes
The children will be able to:
- find the multiplication facts for the 5 times-table.
- recall the multiplication facts for the 5 times-table.
- find the division facts for the 5 times-table.
- recall the division facts for the 5 times-table.

Success criteria
Can the children…

… recall multiplication facts for the 5 times-table:

$6 \times 5, 9 \times 5, 3 \times 5, 10 \times 5, 7 \times 5, 2 \times 5, 4 \times 5, 8 \times 5$?

… recall division facts for the 5 times-table:

$40 \div 5, 25 \div 5, 5 \div 5, 15 \div 5, 50 \div 5, 10 \div 5, 30 \div 5, 45 \div 5$?

Resources needed
- A number line from 0 to 50
- A display of the 5 times-table. (Note that we are using the traditional layout of the 5 times-table, e.g. $3 \times 5 = 15$ to represent 'three fives are fifteen'. Some schools may prefer to use 'three fives are fifteen' written as $5 \times 3 = 15$.)

Opportunities for using and applying the skills
- Solving problems involving addition, subtraction, multiplication and division in the context of numbers or money.
- Identifying and recording the information and calculation needed to solve a problem; carrying out the calculations and checking the solutions.
- Describing patterns and relationships involving numbers.
- Presenting information in lists, tables and simple diagrams.

Andrew Brodie: Number Journey for ages 6-7 © A&C Black Publishers Ltd 2008

The 5 times-table and related division facts

Help at home sheet

Child's name: **Date:**

Dear Parents

At school we follow the National Curriculum and the Primary Framework for mathematics. One aspect of our work in mathematics is the learning of number skills, including learning the 5 times multiplication table and the division facts that arise from it. We are keen to involve parents in their children's learning so you may like to help your child by using some of the ideas on this sheet.

National Curriculum

The Primary Framework for mathematics says that Year 2 pupils should:

• derive and recall multiplication facts for the 5 times-table and the related division facts.

You could...

... practise the 5 times-table every day for a week – in the car, when walking, last thing at night before bed-time, first thing in the morning. It's important on each occasion to keep the practice short, perhaps just one or two minutes. Show your child the table below – with practice he/she will need to look at it less.

1 x 5 = 5	one times five is five
2 x 5 = 10	two fives are ten
3 x 5 = 15	three fives are fifteen
4 x 5 = 20	four fives are twenty
5 x 5 = 25	five fives are twenty-five
6 x 5 = 30	six fives are thirty
7 x 5 = 35	seven fives are thirty-five
8 x 5 = 40	eight fives are forty
9 x 5 = 45	nine fives are forty-five
10 x 5 = 50	ten fives are fifty

Once you feel that your child is confident with saying the table, ask random questions such as: "What's six times five?" "Three fives?" "Seven multiplied by five?"

If you feel that your child is able to answer the multiplication questions easily, try some division questions: "How many fives make forty?" "Divide twenty by five."

You may like to let us know how your child gets on with these activities – if so please return this sheet with any comments on the back.

Andrew Brodie: Number Journey for ages 6-7 © A&C Black Publishers Ltd 2008

The 5 times-table and related division facts

Worksheet 1

Name: _____

Date: _____

On this page I am going to make the 5 times-table.

Draw rings around the stars to make groups of 5.

1 x 5 = [____]   one times five is _____

2 x 5 = [____]   two fives are _____

3 x 5 = [____]   three fives are _____

4 x 5 = [____]   four fives are _____

5 x 5 = [____]   five fives are _____

6 x 5 = [____]   six fives are _____

7 x 5 = [____]   seven fives are _____

8 x 5 = [____]   eight fives are _____

9 x 5 = [____]   nine fives are _____

10 x 5 = [____]   ten fives are _____

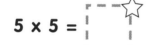
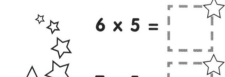

Look at this multiplication fact: 7 x 5 = 35

We can use this fact to find two division facts: 35 ÷ 5 = 7 and 35 ÷ 7 = 5

The 5 times-table and related division facts

Worksheet 2

Name: _____

Date: _____

Look at the 5 times-table. Write division facts next to the multiplication facts. The first 4 have been done for you.

$1 \times 5 = 5$	$\underline{5 \div 5 = 1}$	$\underline{5 \div 1 = 5}$
$2 \times 5 = 10$	$\underline{10 \div 5 = 2}$	$\underline{10 \div 5 = 5}$
$3 \times 5 = 15$	_____	_____
$4 \times 5 = 20$	_____	_____
$5 \times 5 = 25$	_____	There is only one division fact for this one.
$6 \times 5 = 30$	_____	_____
$7 \times 5 = 35$	_____	_____
$8 \times 5 = 40$	_____	_____
$9 \times 5 = 45$	_____	_____
$10 \times 5 = 50$	_____	_____

Fold the paper so that you can't see the 5 times-table!

Can you answer these questions quickly without looking at the 5 times-table?

$6 \times 5 =$	$9 \times 5 =$	$3 \times 5 =$	$10 \times 5 =$
$40 \div 5 =$	$25 \div 5 =$	$5 \div 5 =$	$15 \div 5 =$
$7 \times 5 =$	$2 \times 5 =$	$4 \times 5 =$	$8 \times 5 =$
$50 \div 5 =$	$10 \div 5 =$	$30 \div 5 =$	$45 \div 5 =$

I can...

I can remember the multiplication facts for the 5 times-table. ☐

I can remember the division facts for the 5 times-table. ☐

Andrew Brodie: Number Journey for ages 6-7 © A&C Black Publishers Ltd 2008

The 10 times-table and related division facts

Teacher's notes

Building on previous learning
Before starting this unit check that the children can already:
- count on or back in tens and use this knowledge to derive the multiples of 10 to the tenth multiple.

Learning objectives
- Derive multiplication facts for the 10 times-table.
- Recall multiplication facts for the 10 times-table.
- Derive the related division facts for the 10 times-table.
- Recall the related division facts for the 10 times-table.

Learning outcomes
The children will be able to:
- find the multiplication facts for the 10 times-table.
- recall the multiplication facts for the 10 times-table.
- find the division facts for the 10 times-table.
- recall the division facts for the 10 times-table.

Success criteria
Can the children…

… recall multiplication facts for the 10 times-table:

  4 x 10, 9 x 10, 1 x 10, 3 x 10, 5 x 10, 7 x 10, 2 x 10, 8 x 10?

… recall division facts for the 10 times-table:

  80 ÷ 10, 20 ÷ 10, 100 ÷ 10, 40 ÷ 10, 90 ÷ 10, 30 ÷ 10, 60 ÷ 10, 50 ÷ 10?

Resources needed
- A number line from 0 to 100
- A display/poster of the 10 times-table. (Note that we are using the traditional layout of the 10 times-table, e.g. 6 x 10 = 60 to represent 'six tens are sixty'. Some schools may prefer to choose to use 'six tens are sixty' written as 10 x 6 = 60.

Opportunities for using and applying the skills
- Solving problems involving addition, subtraction, multiplication and division in the context of numbers or money.
- Identifying and recording the information and calculation needed to solve a problem; carrying out the calculations and checking the solutions.
- Describing patterns and relationships involving numbers.
- Presenting information in lists, tables and simple diagrams.

Andrew Brodie: Number Journey for ages 6-7 © A&C Black Publishers Ltd 2008

The 10 times-table and related division facts

Help at home sheet

Child's name: Date:

Dear Parents

At school we follow the National Curriculum and the Primary Framework for mathematics. One aspect of our work in mathematics is the learning of number skills, including learning the 10 times multiplication table and the division facts that arise from it. We are keen to involve parents in their children's learning so you may like to help your child by using some of the ideas on this sheet.

National Curriculum

The Primary Framework for mathematics says that Year 2 pupils should:

- derive and recall multiplication facts for the 10 times-table and the related division facts.

You could...

… practise the 10 times-table every day for a week – in the car, when walking, last thing at night before bed-time, first thing in the morning. It's important on each occasion to keep the practice short, perhaps just one or two minutes. Show your child the table below – with practice he/she will need to look at it less. Many children find the 10 times-table the easiest one of all to learn.

1 x 10 = 10	one times ten is ten
2 x 10 = 20	two tens are twenty
3 x 10 = 30	three tens are thirty
4 x 10 = 40	four tens are forty
5 x 10 = 50	five tens are fifty
6 x 10 = 60	six tens are sixty
7 x 10 = 70	seven tens are seventy
8 x 10 = 80	eight tens are eighty
9 x 10 = 90	nine tens are ninety
10 x 10 = 100	ten tens are one hundred

Once you feel that your child is confident with saying the table, ask random questions such as: "What's seven times ten?" "Three tens?" "Five multiplied by ten?"

If you feel that your child is able to answer the multiplication questions easily, try some division questions: "How many tens make a hundred?" "Divide sixty by ten."

You may like to let us know how your child gets on with these activities – if so please return this sheet with any comments on the back.

Andrew Brodie: Number Journey for ages 6-7 © A&C Black Publishers Ltd 2008

The 10 times-table and related division facts

Worksheet 1

Name: _____

Date: _____

On this page I am going to make the 10 times-table.

Draw rings around the triangles to make groups of 10.

Write the 10 times-table.

1 x 10 = 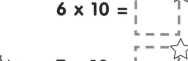   one times ten is _____

2 x 10 = ☆   two tens are _____

3 x 10 = ☆   three tens are _____

4 x 10 = ☆   four tens are _____

5 x 10 = ☆   five tens are _____

6 x 10 = ☆   six tens are _____

7 x 10 = ☆   seven tens are _____

8 x 10 = ☆   eight tens are _____

9 x 10 = ☆   nine tens are _____

10 x 10 = 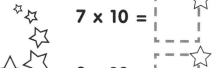   ten tens are _____

Look at this multiplication fact: 9 x 10 = 90

We can use this fact to find two division facts: 90 ÷ 10 = 9 and 90 ÷ 9 = 10

Andrew Brodie: Number Journey for ages 6-7 © A&C Black Publishers Ltd 2008

The 10 times-table and related division facts

Worksheet 2

Name: _____

Look at the 10 times-table. Write division facts next
to the multiplication facts. The first 4 have been done for you.

1 x 10 = 10	10 ÷ 10 = 1	10 ÷ 1 = 10
2 x 10 = 20	20 ÷ 10 = 2	20 ÷ 2 = 10
3 x 10 = 30	_____	_____
4 x 10 = 40	_____	_____
5 x 10 = 50	_____	_____
6 x 10 = 60	_____	_____
7 x 10 = 70	_____	_____
8 x 10 = 80	_____	_____
9 x 10 = 90	_____	_____
10 x 10 = 100	_____	There is only one division fact for this one.

Fold the paper so that you can't see the ten times-table!

Can you answer these questions quickly without looking at the 10 times-table?

4 x 10 =   9 x 10 =   1 x 10 =   3 x 10 =

80 ÷ 10 =   20 ÷ 10 =   100 ÷ 10 =   40 ÷ 10 =

5 x 10 =   7 x 10 =   2 x 10 =   8 x 10 =

90 ÷ 10 =   30 ÷ 10 =   60 ÷ 10 =   50 ÷ 10 =

I can...

I can remember the multiplication facts for the 10 times-table. ☐

I can remember the division facts for the 10 times-table. ☐

Andrew Brodie: Number Journey for ages 6-7 © A&C Black Publishers Ltd 2008